Lucy and the Merman

by AUDREY BRIXNER

illustrated by JOAN BERG VICTOR

SCHOLASTIC BOOK SERVICES

NEW YORK • TORONTO • LONDON • AUCKLAND • SYDNEY • TOKYO

 Published by Scholastic Book Services, a division of Scholastic Magazines, Inc.

12 11 10 9 8 7 6 5 4 3 2 8 9/7 0 1 2/8

01

Printed in the U.S.A.

For Jane Amber Copilow

1

"Oh, nuts!" Lucy sat down on Miss Pennybaker's doorstep. She almost knocked over a plastic bucket that was standing there.

"What a day." Lucy was talking to herself. Her best friend, Nancy, was away. And Lucy's mother was busy. Now Miss Pennybaker wasn't home. Lucy stood up and banged the door knocker three more times.

The little brass knocker looked like an old-fashioned sailing ship. When Lucy banged it, the ship bobbed up and down. "I guess there won't be any sea stories for me today." She stared at the knocker. Then she gave it one last bang.

She had been all set to have her neighbor, Miss Pennybaker, read the sad poem about the merman. Lucy was not sure why she liked the poem. She just did. Sometimes she liked to feel sad.

Lucy almost knew some parts of the poem by heart. She liked the part where the merman sang, "Come away, away children! Come children, come down."

The poem was about a woman who married a merman. A merman lives in the water. He has a fish's tail instead of legs. A merman usually marries a mermaid. But this one had a human wife. She lived with him at the bottom of the sea and had a lot of little mer-children. But one day the mother heard the church bells ringing in her old home town. She told her husband she had to go and swam away home.

She went back to her spinning wheel and back to church. Sometimes she

would think about her children at the bottom of the ocean. But she never saw them again.

Lucy would like to see a merman or a mermaid. And she always kept her eyes open when she went to the beach. But, so far, no luck.

The poem told how the merman and his children swam up to the wife's home town to ask the mother to come back. The children sang to their mother while she was in church. It was a sad song that made Lucy want to cry. But the mother did not even hear it. The father finally told the children to come away. He sang, "Come away, away children! Come children, come down."

It was lucky that the children had a nice father.

"Oh, heck," said Lucy. "I guess I'll go up to the tree house." The tree house was her special place for thinking.

2

The tree house was in a big cherry tree growing in Lucy's yard. The tree was near the house, on the side of a steep hill. At the bottom of the hill and across the road there was a college campus.

It was a beautiful afternoon — fresh and shiny after the rain last night. There were still some puddles on the sidewalk, and lots of the gooey garden slugs that always come out after a rain. Lucy was careful not to step on any of them — ugh!

Lucy climbed up the ladder to the tree house. The tree house was only a platform, but Lucy could feel private up there. Grown-ups did not like to climb the ladder.

Sometimes her friend Nancy came with her. They would play Tarzan or Ali Baba spying down on the forty thieves. But it was spring vacation, and Nancy was away with her family.

As Lucy sat on the platform, she looked all around. She began to sing to herself, "I'm the king of the castle." On the side of the platform near her house she could look down and peek through a little window at the end of the living room. In the living room her mother and her mother's friends were all sitting in a circle.

It was her mother's day to entertain her club. Lucy could see a woman reading out loud. Everybody was listening. Nobody was looking out the little window. They couldn't have seen Lucy, anyhow. She was hidden by the leaves.

Lucy turned around on her platform and looked the other way. Down below she could see the road winding around. There were never many cars early in the afternoon.

Across the road on the campus of the college she could look into a green lake. It seemed to be right below her.

Beyond the campus were miles and miles of houses. She liked to pretend she could see over the houses as far as the Bay Bridge. Somewhere out beyond the bridge was the Pacific Ocean.

Lucy made believe she was up on the mast of a sailing ship staring out to sea. As she looked, she saw, far away, a couple of specks moving in the sky. They came nearer and got larger. Now Lucy could see that the specks were two seagulls.

The larger gull seemed to be chasing the other one. As they got closer, Lucy saw that the smaller bird had something in its mouth. Maybe a fish. Soon the birds were flying right over her tree.

After that she was not sure exactly what happened. First there was a loud crash. Then something fell through the branches. And finally something that felt like a football hit her on the head.

It knocked Lucy flat.

3

Lucy jumped up and waved her arms in front of her face. She thought a bird might be in her hair. Then she looked down. What was that lying on the platform? Was it a fish?

Half of it was a fish. It had a fish's tail. But all the rest was like a little man. It had a tiny head with a curly beard and curly hair. In a way it looked sort of like her brother — if her brother had been about the size of her sneakers.

Lucy did not want to come close to it. Its eyes were closed. And she thought it might be dead. All of a sudden it opened its eyes and spoke to her.

"Sorry to land on you like that." Its voice was so tiny that Lucy had to bend down to hear it. "Thanks for saving my life," it said. "You broke my fall."

Lucy was too surprised to speak. Her legs felt wobbly. For a minute she couldn't say a word. But at last she sat down beside the little creature.

"What are you?" she asked. She might have asked, "Who are you?" except she was not sure whether something that was half fish should be called a who.

It smiled at her. "I'm a merman."

"But I thought mermen were as big as people." Lucy moved closer so she could hear better.

"Some are. Some aren't." The merman sat up and began feeling the back of his head. "We come in all sizes, the same as fish. Besides, I'm still growing."

"Oh." Lucy crossed her legs and made herself comfortable. "How did that gull get hold of you?"

"It was all my fault." The merman seemed to have decided his head was all right. "I was careless. It was such a nice day, and I was sitting on a rock to enjoy the sun and the breeze. Then I noticed my wife below me in the water. She was waving her arms and trying to tell me something. I had to lean over to hear her. That's when that bird grabbed me."

"Maybe she was trying to tell you to watch out." Lucy looked thoughtful.

"Maybe." The merman lay on his stomach and put his chin on his hand. "Anyway, the bird flew away with me. Pretty soon that other bird began to chase us. My bird held onto me and kept flying away from the sea. I said to it,

'Why don't you tell that big bully to mind its own business?' It opened its beak. Anyway, that's how I fell into the tree."

"How did you know how to speak to the bird?" Lucy was full of questions.

"Oh, we mer-people are very good at languages. I don't have any trouble talking to you, do I? I can also talk to fish, of course. And to other creatures, such as otters and sea lions."

"How did you learn all that?" Lucy planned to study French when she got older.

"Well, you see," said the merman, "I have been around a pretty long while — a long while from your way of thinking. I'm still pretty young for a merman. But I'm nearly two hundred."

"Years?" Lucy's eyes almost popped out.

"Yes." The merman laughed at her.

"How long do mermen live?" Lucy knew that elephants live a long time.

"Well, if no accident happens we just go on and on. But, as you see, accidents can happen. A lot of them happen nowadays." He looked sad.

"Yes." Lucy looked down at the road. "We saw a car accident last winter." She moved back so she could rest against the tree trunk. "Do you have a name?"

"Well, we don't have names the way you do. You can call me Triton if you like, T-R-I-T-O-N." It sounded like *try-ton*. Triton wiggled over to the tree too.

"Mr. Triton or just plain Triton?" Lucy wanted to be polite.

"Just plain Triton." He smiled again. "What's your name?"

"Lucy," she said.

"I'm certainly very happy that I bumped into you, Lucy." Triton peeked at her to see if she was going to laugh at his joke. So she laughed politely.

"I wonder how I am going to get home." Triton sighed, and Lucy stared at the floor. "And I am afraid I have already been out of the water too long. My scales are getting awfully itchy. I was not made for living in a tree, you know." Triton looked down at his fishy body.

Lucy tried to think what to do. "Could you sit in a bucket of water?"

"I think so." Triton wiggled still closer to the tree and curled himself up.

"I'll be right back," Lucy said. She climbed down the ladder and ran next door. Miss Pennybaker's plastic bucket was still there.

It was easy to carry the bucket on her arm when it was empty. She was not sure how she could get it up the ladder when it was full of water. If only Nancy were here. She did not want to spoil things by asking any grown-ups for help.

Finally she filled the bucket only half full. That way she could hang it on her arm. At least Triton could sit in it with his fishy part under water. She hauled it up carefully. Then she lifted Triton in.

After a few wiggles he curled his tail around the bottom of the bucket and sat up straight. His head did not quite reach the rim. Nobody but Lucy could see him.

"Thank you very much." Triton stretched his arms around the inside of the bucket. "That's a big help. I hate to bother you, but I'm getting very hungry. I was just going to have breakfast when that gull carried me off."

Lucy looked down through the living room window. She could see her mother giving her friends their cake and coffee. Lucy's mother had promised her a piece of cake. Lucy loved cake. She did not get sweet things very often. Her mother said they were bad for her teeth.

She looked at Triton and asked, "Would you like a piece of cake?" She did her best to sound as though she meant it.

"I don't know till I try." The merman stroked his tail.

Lucy climbed down the ladder and went to get her piece of cake. Carefully she brought it up inside her mother's string shopping bag, which she could hang on her arm.

When she took the cake out of the bag, it was only a little bit crushed. She felt very generous as she held it out to Triton. It was a big piece. Her favorite kind of cake, chocolate. Maybe he would not eat it all.

Triton looked at the cake and poked it with one finger. He took a very small bite. Then he wiped his mouth and handed the cake back to Lucy. He looked the way Lucy looked when her mother wanted her to eat liver.

"Don't you like it?" Lucy tried to act sorry and took the cake back.

"I guess mermen can't eat cake." Triton scraped some crumbs off his tongue. "If only you had a few mussels or some shrimp, and a nice little bit of seaweed for a salad." He licked his lips.

"I'm sorry." Lucy really was sorry. She would have liked to be helpful. She thought and thought. Finally she asked, "Do you like slugs?"

"What are slugs?" He stretched up his head.

"Well, they are nasty slimy squishy things that live in our garden. On days like today they get on the sidewalk too. They are sort of like snails, only without shells."

"They sound nice." Triton smiled and closed his eyes. Then he opened his eyes and looked worried. "You haven't been trying to poison them, have you?"

"No." Lucy shook her head. "My

mother doesn't let us. She doesn't even let us use fertilizer. We don't grow very much in our garden."

"If you are quite sure." Triton put his little palms together like a dog begging. "I would like to try them. Would you get some for me? I'm sorry I'm so helpless. But I'm not much use on land." He looked down at his tail again.

So Lucy climbed down the ladder once more. It was lucky she liked to climb up and down. She did not like slugs, though. And she hated to touch them. But her brother had told her they would not bite or sting. They were just slimy.

Lucy got an empty can. She screwed up her face and went around the garden picking up slugs and putting them into the can. There were lots of green onions. Lucy pulled up a few of them too. She put the can into her string bag to haul it up the ladder.

Triton picked up a slug and smiled as

he turned it around. “It looks tasty. Here goes.” He held the slug like a banana and bit off its head.

Lucy did not feel like eating her chocolate cake just then.

She looked into the living room to see what her mother's friends were doing. They were all talking again.

When she looked back the merman had finished his slug. “I'm sorry to be so greedy,” Triton said. He ate two more. He also ate some of the onions. He said they were nice, especially with slugs.

By now Lucy was beginning to feel better. She was getting used to the idea that mermen eat slugs alive. It did not

seem to bother her any more. So she ate her cake.

Down below, her mother's friends were beginning to leave. One by one they came down the front steps. They looked up into the tree at Lucy and waved. One of them called out, "What are you doing with a bucket up there in the tree, Lucy?" The woman laughed and looked at the other women.

"I needed it," Lucy said.

The woman did not ask any more questions. All the women got into cars and drove down the winding drive to the road below. Soon everyone was gone.

5

Triton sat up on the end of his tail to watch the women drive away. At last, when they were all gone, he sighed. "I wish I could go back to my wife." He looked over the tops of the houses out toward the sea.

"Maybe my father or my brother can drive you to the Bay when they come home." Lucy was looking down at the road.

"Oh no." Triton shook his head. "I don't want any grown-up people to see me. They might want to put me in an aquarium. Or they might cut me up to see what I'm like inside." He swished his tail and looked worried. "But I can't stay here. I need more water than this."

"Well, I could put you in the wash tub in the garage." Lucy wrinkled her forehead. "I don't know how safe it is, though. There's the cat. Once when I put some tadpoles in that tub, somebody came and pulled the plug out."

Triton was only half-listening. He was balancing on his tail to see over the rim of the bucket. "What's that, Lucy?" The merman pounded the bucket and pointed. He was looking down the hill at the green lake on the college campus.

"That's a lake," she said. Lucy stood up too. "Would you like to go down there? It's not the ocean."

"It would be much better for me than a tree." Triton smiled a little. "I would have time to decide what to do next. Do you suppose you could get me down there?"

Lucy stared at the lake and thought hard. "First we have to get you down from this tree. I don't like to go down the ladder with that bucket. Could you ride in my string bag?"

"I could try." Triton felt the string to see how strong it was.

Lucy helped him settle into the bag and dropped the bucket over the side.

"Do you suppose we could bring along

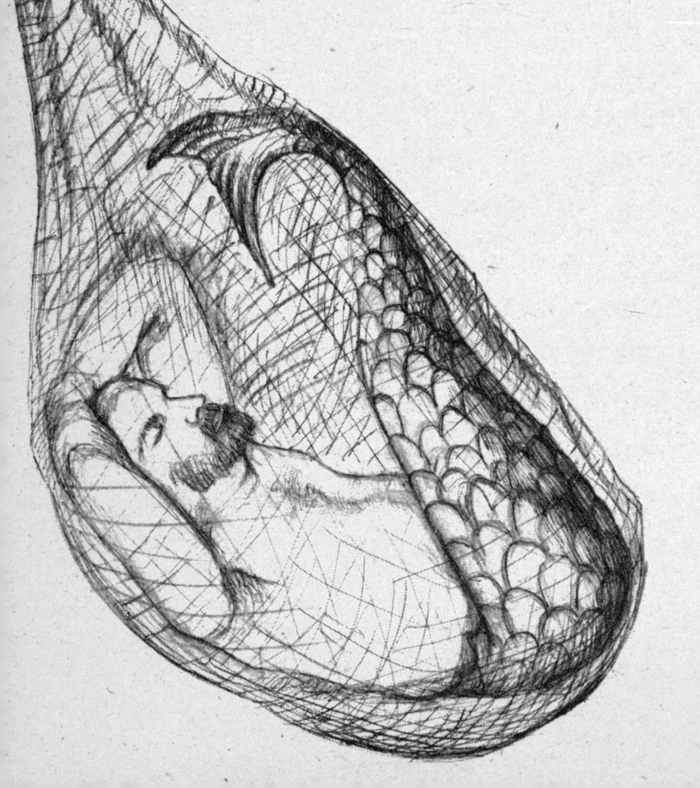

the rest of these tasty slugs?" Triton took the can in his arms.

"I guess so." Lucy tried not to make a face. But she wished he had not thought of it.

She hung the string bag with Triton in it over her shoulder. Luckily he was lighter than her cat. And he was careful not to wiggle. Step by step Lucy went backwards down the ladder. At the bottom she sat down to rest because her knees were trembling.

Lucy filled the bucket again with water from the washtub in the garage. She lifted Triton back into it and handed him the can of slugs. They were ready for their journey.

Lucy ran into the kitchen where her mother was loading the dishwasher. "I'm going down to the campus, Mother."

"All right." Her mother did not look up. "Don't be late for supper."

6

Lucy often went down to the campus, sometimes by herself, sometimes with Nancy. It was a good place to play. There were open fields for running games and patches of woods where they could play Indians, or elves and fairies. And there was a stream with a bridge over it.

Best of all there was the lake. People were not allowed to swim in the lake. But all around it were woods where the girls could play. Sometimes they just liked to sit beside the water and dream.

Lucy picked up the heavy bucket and started down the driveway. It was lucky her mother was in the kitchen and did not see her going off with Miss Pennybaker's bucket.

When she came to the road, Lucy could not hear anything coming. She started across. Just as she reached the middle, she heard a car. Lucy tried to hurry. The bucket swung back and forth. Some of the water sloshed out. It spilled over her jeans and ran into her shoes.

Triton was having trouble staying in the bucket. He was using both hands to hold onto his can of slugs. Every time water sloshed out of the bucket, Triton almost slid out too. In the nick of time he braced himself with his tail. At last they

reached the other side, just before the car rushed past.

Then they rested under a tree. There was no path along this road. But Lucy usually walked on the hard dirt beside the campus fence. Today the dirt was mostly mud after last night's rain. And she wished she had worn her rubber boots. Her sneakers were going *squish-squish*. Before she knew it, one of her shoes had come untied and was starting to pull off in the mud.

While she tied her shoe, she had to put the bucket down. The heavy bucket sank into the mud. When she pulled it out, it made a sucking sound and came out with a sudden jerk. Lucy almost fell backwards into the mud. More water sloshed out of the bucket. Triton whirled around and around clutching his can of slugs. Lucy's shoes and the bucket had wads of mud sticking to them.

At last she reached some grass near the

fence. She used a stick and some grass to scrape off most of the mud. Two big boys were coming along the road with their dog. Lucy stuck the bucket behind a tree and pretended she was only cleaning her shoes.

The dog came over to have a look. He sniffed at Triton. Lucy held her breath. Then one of the boys whistled, and the dog ran after him. Lucy watched the two boys walk around the bend. When they were gone she picked up the bucket again.

She walked along the road. People in cars looked at her carrying the bucket. But they did not stop. Lucy soon reached the back gate to the campus. She walked down the footpath that led to the fields and buildings below. Now she felt safer. It was spring vacation, and there were not many students around. Before long she reached the path that went through the woods to the lake.

7

Lucy had a favorite rock beside the lake where she liked to come after school and sit by herself. She would sit there watching a family of long-legged water bugs dancing round and round on top of the water. Sometimes she thought she could just sit there forever. But at the end of the afternoon she always remembered to go home for dinner.

Today she brought Triton to her rock. As soon as she lifted him out of the bucket he dropped the can of slugs and slid into the water. It all happened so fast that Lucy hardly had time to blink. He could have said thank you, or at least good-bye. She sat looking at the spot where he had disappeared.

At last she stood up. "Guess I might as well go home," she said out loud. She put the can of slugs on a ledge near the water before she picked up the bucket. Then she stepped onto the path.

"Don't go." She heard Triton's tiny voice behind her. At once Lucy came back to the rock. Triton hauled himself out of the water. "I'm sorry I rushed off that way." Triton curled up on the rock. "I just had to get down under water for a while." He pointed to the rock beside him. Lucy started to sit down.

Just then the campus tower clock began to strike. They could hear it through the woods. It was striking the quarter hour. Every fifteen minutes it would strike. Once at the quarter hour, twice at half past, and three times at quarter to. On the hour it would do it four times. Then it would strike the time.

"It's only quarter past four," Lucy said. "I don't have to go home until five o'clock."

She sat down on the rock. "Tell me what it's like at the bottom of the sea. Do you live in sand-strewn caverns and sit on golden thrones?" That's how the merman and his wife in the poem had lived.

"Well, not exactly." Triton smiled. "It's hard to explain." He leaned on his elbow and stared at the sky. "In the first place, we don't live at the very bottom of the ocean. That's too far down. At the bottom it's too dark. And we like to come up to the top sometimes. So we have safe sleeping places that float around under water. We can go deep down when we want to, but we don't live at the very bottom."

Lucy tried to think what it would be like to live in a home that was floating under water. She did not think she would like it. She decided to ask something else. "Do you have any children?"

"Yes, we have four children. They are all out on their own now, except the youngest." He sighed.

"Why do you look sad?" Lucy thought he was sad because his children were grown.

"I am thinking about my youngest daughter." Triton sighed again. "It's because of her that my wife and I came to this part of the sea."

"What's the matter with her?" Lucy put her hands around her knees. She had the feeling she was going to hear something exciting.

8

"My daughter is lost." Triton sighed again.

"How did she get lost?" Lucy had got lost herself once.

"It's a long story." Triton stared at the lake. Lucy watched the water bugs until Triton began talking. "I'm afraid we spoiled her. It's hard not to spoil the youngest. She's very pretty. And mermaids like to be pretty. In the old days pretty mermaids used to be good at wrecking ships."

"Wrecking ships?" Lucy was shocked.

"Yes." Triton did not notice the look on Lucy's face. "They would swim up to the surface and dance around ships singing beautiful songs. The sailors would look at them and listen to them and forget to watch where they were going. Sometimes the ships ran onto rocks. Other times they got caught in whirlpools."

"That was wicked." Lucy sat up straight and frowned. She moved away from Triton.

"I guess maybe it was." Triton tried to look ashamed. He moved over to where Lucy was. "Most mer-people do not like land people."

"Why not?" Lucy went on frowning.

"I don't mean people like you. I mean other people. We have lots of reasons. I'd better get back to telling you about Sabrina."

"Is that her name, Sabrina?" Lucy tried not to show she thought that was a funny name. Triton was a funny name too.

"Yes. Lots of mermaids are called Sabrina." Triton stared at a tree. "Well, to get back. Sabrina was one of those beautiful children that everyone makes a fuss over. You know how that is." Triton looked at Lucy.

Lucy nodded.

Triton went on talking. "Sabrina got in the habit of thinking she could do whatever she wanted. She thought everything was always going to be easy for her and would turn out all right. Usually everything did." Triton paused and rubbed his hands against the rock.

He began talking again. "She did not pay enough attention to her teachers. Mer-people have to learn their lessons. It is very important because the sea is not a safe place. It is a nice place. But it is not a safe place. We have to learn to take care of ourselves." He looked out at the lake some more. Lucy wished he would hurry up.

He sighed again. "Sabrina was always

talking about how she would grow up and be a siren."

"A siren? What's that?" In her mind Lucy was hearing the siren on a fire truck.

"In the old days mermaids were sometimes called sirens, especially the beautiful ones, the ones who were good at wrecking ships." Triton threw a pebble into the water. "We could never get it into Sabrina's head that she was still too small to be a siren. The real sirens are big, as big as land people. That means they are very old. The longer we live, the bigger we get. The bigger we get, the more we know."

"I guess that's why you got caught by a gull." Lucy looked down at Triton.

"I guess so." Triton smiled a tiny smile. "Anyway, ships nowadays are too big to notice mermaids of any size. But that didn't bother Sabrina. She spent her time planning to be a siren and did not work hard learning languages. She could not even swim as fast as she should for her age. We have to learn to swim very fast and be good at team swimming. That takes a lot of training. She was good at singing, though. I will admit that." Triton smiled to himself.

"The worst was that she did not like her mother or me to tell her what to do. You probably know about that." Triton looked at Lucy again.

Lucy nodded.

Triton sat still for a while. He started talking again. "She kept begging us to let her go traveling. Then, a while back, some young mer-people were going on a trip. They planned to swim up and down the California coast. We mer-people travel a lot. But we know how to watch out for danger. Sabrina thought she was grown up when really she wasn't."

"How old is she?" Lucy's brother was almost twenty.

"She isn't even eighty yet." Triton helped himself to a slug and started chewing on it. He peeked up at Lucy and laughed a little. Then he went on. "What happened was that she just went anyway."

"Why didn't you go along?" Lucy always had her family with her when she went on trips.

"I wish we had." Triton sighed some more. "We did not want to go on a trip just then. Besides, she wanted to go without us." This time he sat still so long Lucy thought he was never going to get going again.

He flipped a pebble into the water as he talked. "All the others came back after a while. But Sabrina was not with them. Nobody knew what happened to her. The last anyone saw of her was somewhere out beyond the Golden Gate Bridge. They were swimming around on the surface. Just then they saw a big tanker coming. And they all dived down in a hurry. Later, they noticed Sabrina was missing. They stayed around for a week to look for her. Then they came home."

"What's a tanker?" Lucy had a picture in her mind of the row of tanks at the gas station.

"It's an enormous ship, the kind that carries oil." Triton was silent for a while. Lucy wished she could help.

"So then you and your wife came to look for her, and instead you got picked up by that gull." Lucy looked at Triton.

"That's about it." Triton seemed a little bit ashamed. "I wasn't so smart myself that time. My wife and I didn't come alone, though. Mer-people usually travel in groups. It's safer that way. I suppose everybody is wondering now if they will ever see me again." This time he looked up at the sky.

Just then the clock began striking five.

"Oh, I have to go." Lucy stood up slowly. She always hated to stop in the middle of a story.

"Can you come back tomorrow?" Triton began to slide down the rock toward the water.

"I think so, but not till after lunch." Lucy knew she had to take her music lesson in the morning. And she also had to practice.

"All right. You come after lunch. I'll be waiting for you. Sing me a song when you want me to come up." Triton slid into the water and disappeared.

9

The next day, Lucy gobbled her lunch and ran down to the lake. When she reached her rock, everything looked the same as usual. A couple of birds were flying overhead. The water bugs were going round and round on top of the water. And down below she could see some fish swimming. But there was no sign of Triton.

She wondered if he really would come or if she had only imagined the whole thing. "Triton," she called. She kept her voice soft because she did not want anyone to hear.

"Sing me a song when you want me to

come," he had said. What kind of song? Lucy thought and thought but could not think of a single song.

For a while she sat looking at the water bugs. She looked at them so long that her eyes went dim. She felt like crying. Then suddenly she remembered the words of a song. "*Flow gently sweet Afton among thy green braes.*" That gave Lucy an idea.

She sang in a low voice. "Oh Triton, sweet Triton among thy green waves, come quickly I'll sing thee a song in thy praise."

"That's a nice start," said Triton. "What's the praise going to be?" He pulled himself onto the rock and flipped the water off his tail.

"Oh, Triton, I was afraid you weren't coming. I really don't know what comes next in that song. But I'm so glad to see you again."

"That's praise enough for me." Triton

smiled at her. He looked much more cheerful than he had yesterday. "This is a really nice lake. I have been swimming all around in it. I even swam down the stream that goes through the campus, in fact." He took a deep breath. Lucy waited to hear what he was going to say next. "In fact, I think I have found a way back to the sea."

"You have?" Lucy was really surprised. She knew that all around the campus wall there were streets and houses.

"The stream goes underground. I followed it down to where it goes into the Bay. Then I came back because I promised you I'd be here." He looked down at the empty can where the slugs had been.

"I guess you'll be leaving. And I'll never see you again." Lucy felt sorry.

"How would you like to come for a little swim with me?" Triton held out his hand.

"We aren't allowed to swim in this lake." Lucy pointed to the signs that said, "No Swimming" and "No Fishing." "And besides, it's too cold to go swimming."

"If you come with me," Triton said, "you won't need to worry about anything. You won't feel cold. And that 'No Swimming' sign is not talking about fish — or about mermen or mermaids."

Lucy looked down at her blue jeans. "I'm not a mermaid."

"How would you like to be a mermaid just for one afternoon? I promise to get you back by five o'clock."

"How can you make me a mermaid?" Lucy looked down at Triton. He was smiling up at her.

"When I'm in the water I can do all sorts of things. It's only when I'm on land that I'm helpless." Triton leaned back and waited.

"I don't really think I should." Lucy looked worried.

"You don't need to worry." Triton smiled again. "After what you've done for me, I wouldn't let anything happen to you."

"What about seagulls?" asked Lucy.

"Don't you worry," Triton said again. "Don't you want to have an adventure?" Down deep Lucy knew she did. "Come with me and I'll show you how the merpeople live." Triton spread out his hands. "You'll never get a chance like this again."

"But how can you do all that before five o'clock?" Lucy frowned.

"Our time is not the same as your time." Triton stretched out his arm.

"Sometimes it's longer. Sometimes it's shorter. We'll have lots of time."

Lucy was running out of excuses. But she was still not sure she liked the idea.

"There's only one thing you have to be careful about." Triton took hold of her pant leg. He looked serious. "You must not eat anything while you are with us. If you do you might have to stay a mermaid. I promise that you won't feel hungry."

Lucy thought about the slugs. She was sure she could promise not to eat anything. But still she sat on the rock and stared at the water bugs. Almost in a dream she seemed to hear Triton's little voice singing, "Come away, away Lucy! Come Lucy, come down."

Before she knew what she was doing, she had slipped off the rock. The water felt soft and cool, not really cold. Lucy started to swim the way she usually did. She was a good swimmer.

"Not that way, Lucy," Triton said, "like this."

Now Lucy saw that she was not a little girl any more. She was a tiny mermaid. Instead of her blue jeans she had a scaly blue body. Where her sneakers had been, there was a little white tail.

10

"Point your arms over your head and wiggle your body from side to side, like this." Triton showed her how. They practiced, going round and round the lake until Lucy got the feel of it. What a nice way to swim. She did not have to worry about breathing at all. And she did not get tired. Triton showed her how to roll over onto her back and float under water. That way she could look up at the trees and the sky. The trees looked wavy and misty. Everything up there looked sort of funny.

"Now we are ready to start down the stream." Triton led her to the part of the lake where the stream was. It was very full because the rainy season was not quite over.

"We have to be a little bit careful going through campus." Triton stopped at the beginning of the stream to explain what they had to do. "We won't go very fast. And we'll go one at a time. We have to stay close to the bottom and close to the bank so no one will notice us." Lucy nodded. Then Triton started down the stream, with Lucy swimming a little way behind. When they saw something growing in the stream, they headed for it. They could hide there while they looked around.

The bridge was just ahead. Triton pulled Lucy close to the bank and made her wait. People were standing in the middle of the bridge. They were talking. It seemed to take them forever to decide to go. After that, the stream went through a part of the campus where people did not walk much. At last they came to the spot where the creek went underground. It was a place that Lucy had never noticed before. All of a sudden the water went into a big pipe.

"Now we can go faster." Triton stopped while Lucy caught up with him. "I will show you how mer-people swim when they travel in groups. You get behind me. Hold on to my tail. And try to wiggle the way I do. That's all you have to do. I will go slowly at first."

Lucy took hold of Triton's tail. They started down the tunnel. The water was dark. But soon Lucy noticed that there was a faint light. It took a while for her to realize the light was coming from her own forehead. There was just enough so she could see a little way around her. She noticed that there were fish in the tunnel. There were even a few plants. She began to realize that they were going faster and faster.

Fish seemed to be flying by in the other direction. Lucy felt as though she was in a subway train rushing under the Bay. She liked going fast. And she was having no trouble holding onto Triton and wiggling the way he had shown her.

Sometimes there was a rush of water that told her other streams were coming into the tunnel. After a while the tunnel got larger. And up ahead she could see light. Triton was slowing down. As it got brighter and brighter, Triton stopped.

"We are going into a stream that leads into the Bay. I want to look around before we plunge in." He looked out into the water.

"Not much around right now," he said, "only fish. We are lucky. Hold on. I'm going to speed up. We'll stop again when we get to the entrance to the Bay."

To Lucy it seemed hardly any time at all before they reached the next stop.

"Now we will have to be more careful until we get out into the ocean. I'll stay close to the bottom." Triton headed toward the Bay Bridge and Treasure Island. He was still going fast and seemed to be able to dodge around fish without even thinking. The water here was not clean. No one up above would be able to see them. Triton told Lucy to keep her mouth closed until they got out of the Bay.

Before she knew what had happened, they had shot under the Golden Gate Bridge and were out in the Pacific Ocean. The water now was a little bit colder. Out here, Lucy could look up through the water and see the sky.

"The next thing is to look for my wife." Triton headed for some rocks not far from the shore.

11

A big rock stuck up out of the water. Triton dived down to the very bottom of it. It seemed a long way down. The sky looked far away. Lucy could no longer hear the wind. Down there they found a few fish but no mer-people.

"I guess she got tired of waiting." Triton swam all around the rock. "When we lose each other we try to head for the last place where we were together. I hope everybody hasn't gone home."

A large flat fish lay on the ocean floor. Triton went over and said something to it. Lucy could not understand what he said or what the fish said. But when he came back he was smiling. "It's all right."

Triton put his fists in front of his mouth, one in front of the other. Then he blew. He sounded as if he was blowing a little horn.

All of a sudden Lucy could see dark shapes in the water coming from all sides. In a minute she was in the middle of about twenty mer-people. They were all sizes and all colors. Some were blue, some red, some black. Some were silvery like Triton. Some were as big as her father, some were bigger. And some were even smaller than Triton and Lucy.

They were so glad to see Triton that everybody tried to talk at once. And Triton only laughed at them. At the same time they were looking at Lucy the way people look when they expect to be introduced.

A silvery mer-woman swam out of the crowd. She rushed at Triton and gave him a hug. Then she began to scold him. "You really had me scared this time. I have told you and told you not to sit on rocks by yourself. I can't let you out of my sight for a minute."

Triton laughed and patted her on the arm. "I should have listened to you. If it had not been for Lucy here, I don't know what would have happened. She saved my life." He pulled Lucy out from behind him and introduced his wife. "Lucy, this is my wife, Thetis."

Thetis was a beautiful mer-woman. Even when she was angry she was beautiful. But now she stopped frowning and hugged Lucy. For a long time she did not say anything. Then she said, "That Triton simply has to have a woman watching him all the time." She looked at Triton again. "Tell us what happened."

"Well, to make a long story short, that bird dropped me into a tree where Lucy just happened to be sitting. Lucy is really a little girl, in case you haven't guessed." Everybody looked at Lucy with surprise.

And Triton did not explain what Lucy was doing sitting in a tree. He just said, "Lucy helped me get down from there and into a lake. From the lake I was able to swim here. I'll tell you the rest later."

"Is Lucy going to come and live with us?" Thetis kept her arm around Lucy's shoulders.

"No. No, she is just visiting." Triton looked seriously at all the mer-people. They nodded. Then they all wanted to come up and shake Lucy's hand. Lucy felt very important.

After the hand shaking was over, Thetis waited until everybody was quiet. "We have a surprise for you, Triton."

"What's that?" Triton looked around. But he did not see anything surprising.

Then Thetis swam to the other side of the rock and came back with a small mermaid. The mermaid was streaked all over with some greenish-gray stuff. Her hair was stuck together in wads. Triton stared at her for a minute. Then he shouted, "Sabrina" and hugged her so hard her tail floated over her head. "But what happened to you?" He let go of her and looked her over. "Why are you so dirty?" Sabrina began to cry.

"Don't pester her, Triton." Thetis put her arm around Sabrina. "It wasn't her

fault. And she's had a bad time."

Triton looked ashamed. "Where did you find her?"

"Proteus found her." Thetis pointed to a huge gray merman who was floating around in the back of the group.

Proteus swam up. "I found her over by the Golden Gate Bridge."

For some reason, that made Thetis frown at Triton again. "He had just brought her here when that bird grabbed you." Then Thetis thought of something and stopped frowning. "Maybe it was my fault you got caught. I was trying to make you come down. And you were listening to me instead of watching out."

"Well, all's well that ends well," said Triton. "I'm so glad to have Sabrina back no matter how messy she looks." This time when he smiled at Sabrina she smiled back a little. "Aren't you going to tell me what happened?" Triton tried to take hold of Sabrina's hand, but she swam around behind her mother.

"Don't make fun of her, Triton. She has had a nasty time sitting under that bridge. She is all covered with oil. And she can't swim very well. She has been living on mussels and wondering what was going to happen to her." Thetis stroked Sabrina's oily hair.

"Where did the oil come from?" Triton looked at Sabrina's greeny-gray face.

"It came from that tanker. Sabrina was practicing being a siren. She was swimming behind the ship and singing. But nobody on the ship noticed her. And all of a sudden a big patch of oil leaked out. It completely covered her. For a while she could not breathe and thought she was going to die.

"Luckily the tide pushed her up against the bridge. Otherwise we would never have seen her again." Thetis held on to Sabrina. And Triton looked serious. Lucy tried not to stare at Sabrina.

12

"Well." Triton looked around at all the other mer-people. "Maybe we can think about heading for home now. What do you say?"

"Fine." Proteus swam over to the rock. Behind him people began to form a line. Proteus seemed to be the leader. Lucy watched as the mer-people arranged themselves according to size. It was like a string of beads. At the head of the line was Proteus with four other big mer-people behind him.

"The big mer-people are the oldest. They can swim the fastest." Triton took Lucy's hand. "I'll go in front of you. And

Thetis will go after. Sabrina will follow Thetis." Behind Sabrina the smaller mer-people were lining themselves up.

"Everybody ready?" Proteus glanced back over the line to see how it looked. "All right, Triton, you can blow your horn." Triton put his hands together and blew. This time the horn sounded to Lucy something like a train whistle.

"Hold on to my tail, Lucy." Triton stretched out his arms and caught hold of the tail of the mermaid in front of him. Lucy grabbed Triton's tail. And Thetis held on to Lucy. The train began to move.

At first it crept along, the way a train does when it leaves the station. Then it began to go fast. The big mer-people did most of the pulling. But everybody helped. They were all wiggling from side to side as they swam. The line of swimmers looked something like an eel.

Lucy tried to do what Triton was doing. And Thetis helped her from behind. Soon they were going faster and faster. They must surely be going as fast as a jet plane. After they had been swimming for a while, somebody up front began to sing. Soon everybody was singing. It was not a song that Lucy knew. And she could not make out the words. If she had not known the mer-people were singing, she might have thought she was hearing the wind. But she knew she was too far down in the water for that.

All of a sudden the singing stopped. And the line of swimmers began to slow down. Instead of the singing, Lucy could hear a murmur coming down the line.

"Detour ahead. Fishing ships. Pass it on." Triton turned his head and spoke to Lucy.

So Lucy turned her head and said to Thetis, "Detour ahead. Fishing ships. Pass it on."

Suddenly they swooped down through

black, black water. They dropped so fast Lucy's ears stopped working. She had to swallow over and over before any sound would come. Ahead of her she saw that the line of lights in the mer-people's foreheads had all run together. The lights were streaking along like a colored snake.

At last the swimmers stopped going down and began to move ahead. But still they went so fast Lucy did not have time to think. Little by little she saw the water change color from black to navy blue.

Triton turned his head. "We're almost there." In fact, they were slowing down. And bit by bit they stopped. They were still out in the middle of the ocean and way under water. But the line of swimmers seemed to be getting shorter. Where had everybody gone? Lucy could only see that there were not so many lights up ahead.

"Here we go." Triton suddenly dived

straight down. He pulled Lucy after him. She saw that they had come through a door in the roof of a big hall. "You can let go now." Triton had stopped holding on to the mermaid in front of him. And Thetis let go of Lucy's tail.

The hall was very big. Tiny fish with lamps in their heads were swimming everywhere. They made enough light so that Lucy could see the hall was full of mer-people. There must have been at least a hundred. The mer-people all came swimming around Proteus and Triton.

They looked at Lucy and Sabrina and wanted to know what had happened. It took a little while for Triton and Proteus to tell the story.

13

"One of our poets will make a poem about you one of these days," Triton said as he smiled at Lucy. And Lucy thought about Miss Pennybaker's merman poem.

All the mer-people seemed to want to come up and speak to Lucy. It was nice to feel so important. One little merman who was about the same size she was kept swimming around waiting for a chance to speak to her. He had a tan body and a blue tip to his tail. He and Lucy were the only ones with the tips of their tails a different color from the rest of their tails.

"This is Daniel." Triton put his hand on Daniel's shoulder. "Daniel was once a little boy."

Daniel smiled at Lucy. "Are you going to stay with us?"

"No, I have to be home by five o'clock. Don't you have to go home?" Lucy looked worried.

"No, I can't go home. I can't live on land any more." Daniel went on smiling. He had a nice smile.

"Why not?" Lucy was frowning a little.

"I didn't come the way you came. I fell out of a boat. Proteus rescued me and brought me here. My family all thought I was drowned."

Lucy was shocked. "Well, I still don't see why you can't go back." She did not smile.

"The only way Proteus could rescue me was to turn me into a merman. Otherwise I would have drowned. Besides, that was many years ago. My family are all gone now." Lucy wondered why Daniel still looked like a little boy.

Triton looked at Lucy. "I told you, Lucy, that time down here is not the

same as time where you live." Then he said, "I'm going to leave you with Daniel for a while. He can show you around. Thetis and I have to take Sabrina to the doctor."

"Come on, Lucy." Daniel began to swim through the crowd of mer-people. Lucy swam after him. All the mer-people smiled and waved as she went by. Daniel swam as far as the wall where they could be away from most of the others.

The wall seemed to be made of glass.

Lucy could see right through it. She could see fish going by on the other side. The fish were all shapes and sizes and colors. They did not seem to come close to the wall. The wall was thick, but it was also soft, like some kind of skin. Lucy thought it would be fun just to float and watch the fish.

"I wish you would stay with us." Daniel stared out at the fish.

"I can't." Lucy shook her head.

"Why not? It's awfully nice down

here. We travel a lot. And we don't have to go to school." Daniel looked to see what Lucy thought about that.

"I can't because I can't." Lucy moved a little way away from Daniel. "Why don't you have to go to school? Triton said mer-people have to learn a lot of things."

"We do, but we don't have to learn them in school." Daniel rolled over on his back and put his hands behind his head.

"Oh, what's that?" Lucy suddenly forgot about everything else. She pointed at a strange red creature going by. It looked as long as a bus. Where its mouth should be, it had a lot of wavy things. And it looked fierce.

Daniel laughed. "That's a squid. Stick around a while and you'll see a lot of things you never saw before."

Lucy remembered they were talking about school. "If you don't have to go to school, how do you learn things?"

"We have teachers. They take us around with them one at a time and show us how to do things. It's more fun than school. We have lots of time, you know. We don't learn everything all at once." Daniel swam in a circle around Lucy.

"Don't people have to grow up and go to work?" Lucy knew she would have to go to work when she grew up.

"Not the kind of work you are thinking about." Daniel smiled. "For one thing, we never stop growing. Our work is learning things. We have to remember everything because we don't have any books."

Lucy thought it would be strange not to have any books. "What are you studying?" She remembered that Triton had said they had to learn swimming and languages and music.

"Right now I'm learning music. I'm not very good at it yet." Daniel pointed at a funny looking pink fish that was swimming toward them. Then he went on. "The mer-people like music a lot."

"Why don't people go to work?" Lucy looked around at the hall full of people. Some were lying around talking. Some were playing musical instruments. Some were eating.

"We don't have any trouble finding food. And we don't need anything else." Daniel looked down at his scaly body.

"What do you eat?" Lucy knew right away that she should not have asked that.

"We eat a lot of small things, like shrimp. Many people just eat a gooey sort of cold stew. We don't cook anything, of course." Daniel laughed at the face Lucy made. "The stew is really very nice. You get used to it fast. Like to try some? I'll get it for you." Daniel looked as though he was about to swim off toward a part of the hall where people were eating.

"No thanks, I'm not hungry." Lucy was telling the truth. She really wasn't hungry.

"What are they eating out of?" Lucy could see that the people were holding little bowls in their hands.

"Some are eating out of shells. And some are using bowls. We find lots of bowls in wrecked ships. There are all sorts of things lying at the bottom of the sea." Daniel looked through the floor of the hall. There were fish swimming down there too.

When she looked around again, Lucy saw that the hall was nearly empty. "Where has everybody gone?"

"Oh, I forgot. Tonight is the night of the full moon. Come on." Daniel pulled Lucy by the hand and began to swim up toward the roof.

14

Lucy pulled her hand away. "If the moon is out, I should be home."

Daniel laughed. "The moon isn't out yet in your part of the world. Come on."

Just then Triton and Thetis came swimming toward them. "Oh, here you are, Lucy. Come with us." They began to follow Daniel.

"Where are we going?" Lucy followed Thetis.

"Up on the roof to look at the moon," Thetis said.

"What happens when there is a full moon?" Lucy had to wiggle hard to keep up.

Thetis smiled. "Nothing happens. We just like to look at the moon. And we like

to come up at night and sit in the air."
She zoomed up through a hole in the roof.

Lucy swam up behind her. Somehow the big hall had risen up almost to the top of the water. It must have happened while she was talking to Daniel. She wanted to ask how it did that. But everybody was so quiet she decided to wait until later.

The mer-people were all sitting on the roof with their tails in the water and their heads and arms in the air. It was a quiet

night. As far as Lucy could see there was nothing but miles and miles of water. The breeze was hardly a breeze at all, and the waves were very small. As Lucy sat on the roof beside Thetis and Triton, she rocked gently up and down with the waves. Daniel sat with them. But he did not talk.

Everybody sat looking at the moon, which seemed to be coming out of the water very large and orange. It seemed to be sliding up the edge of the sky. A long line of moonlight was spreading itself on the water, like a golden road that went right up to the moon. There was no sound of talking.

But there was music. Some of the mer-people were playing instruments. It was soft music that came from little flutes they were blowing. Sometimes the music sounded like wind in the trees. Sometimes it sounded like birds getting ready to go to bed.

Everyone was so quiet that Lucy felt a little bit sleepy. And Thetis let her lean against her shoulder. Lucy went on looking at the moon and listening to the music. She did not know why she felt so happy. Her head began to nod. Maybe she went to sleep for a little while.

Suddenly she heard a lot of noise. Everybody was moving. Thetis pulled Lucy down through a hole in the roof. All the mer-people came diving down one after the other.

"What's the matter?" Lucy was wide awake.

"A whale." Thetis swam toward the back wall. And Lucy wiggled after her. Inside the hall, the mer-people were now swimming around. They were not excited any more.

Thetis showed Lucy a dark shape as big as a house diving down toward the bottom of the ocean. It took a long time to go by. In the moonlight Lucy could see it clearly. But she could not see its eye. She remembered the part in the merman poem where it talked about how "great whales come sailing by, sail and sail, with unshut eye." Do whales ever go to sleep? Lucy wondered.

Lucy was feeling sleepy again. And the big hall was growing quiet. The lights from the little fishes looked dim and fuzzy. The moonlight was all around her. Thetis showed Lucy how to curl up on her side. Lucy closed her eyes and went to sleep.

15

When she opened her eyes it was already light. The water outside the hall was pale green. The sunlight was coming down through the water. Thetis was gone. But Daniel was sitting beside her holding a big shell.

"I wondered how long you were going to sleep." Daniel laughed as Lucy sat up and rubbed her eyes. She did not quite remember where she was. That made Daniel laugh some more. "Don't you want some breakfast?" He held out the shell, which was full of something soupy and slimy.

"No thank you. I'm not hungry." Lucy wondered why she was not hungry. But she was glad she wasn't.

"All right, if that's the way you feel." And Daniel swallowed the soupy stuff himself. Then he let the shell slide through the water down toward the bottom of the hall. Lucy looked surprised.

"When we want a dish, we just swim down there and get one." Daniel wiped the corners of his mouth with his fingers.

"That isn't very clean. Don't you have to wash them?" Lucy thought Daniel was being sloppy.

"You talk like a land person. We don't have to worry about things like that." Daniel rolled over on his back and stared at the roof.

Lucy changed the subject. "How did you fall out of that boat?" She remembered that Daniel was down here because he had fallen out of a boat.

"I was out in a rowboat with my parents one time when we were in Monterey on our vacation. We didn't know very much about boats. And the weather began to get stormy. A big wave hit the boat and turned it over. I didn't know how to swim very well in those days." Daniel did some cartwheels in the water.

"Didn't you have on a vest?" Lucy always had to wear a life vest when she went out in a boat.

"We didn't have things like that. This was a long time ago." Daniel stopped swimming and lay still.

"What happened to your parents?" Lucy kept asking questions.

"Proteus told me that they hung onto the boat until somebody came and helped them." Daniel was looking out at the fish.

"Why didn't you hang onto the boat?" Lucy thought she would have known enough to do that.

"I guess I got muddled." Daniel did not look at Lucy. "And, besides, the boat hit me on the head when it turned over. It's just lucky for me that Proteus and some other mer-people were swimming nearby." Daniel rubbed his head.

"What did your parents do?" Lucy thought about her mother.

"There wasn't anything they could do. They looked for me and waited around for me to wash up on the beach. Finally they had to go home." Daniel pretended to be looking at the fish.

"Why didn't you tell them where you were?" Lucy thought Daniel could at least have done that.

"At first I couldn't because I had to wait for my head to get well. By that time they were not anywhere near the sea. They lived in El Paso, Texas. Besides, they wouldn't have believed me. Let's talk about something else." Daniel frowned.

Just then Lucy saw Thetis and Triton swimming toward her. They had Sabrina with them.

"I see Daniel has found you again."

Triton smiled. "Did you have a good sleep?" He was holding Sabrina's hand.

Lucy smiled at Triton and Thetis. "Is Sabrina feeling better?" She could see that Sabrina was still covered with greenish-gray streaks. But some silver spots were beginning to shine through.

"It will take a while for her to get back to normal." Triton put his arm around Sabrina's shoulders. But Sabrina did not say anything. She looked through the wall behind Lucy as if Lucy were not there.

"Here we are, already." Thetis was looking out at the sea.

Lucy was surprised. She looked where Thetis was looking, but all she saw at first was fish. Then she saw a dark shape and wondered if it was another whale. She looked at Triton.

"We are going to Neptune's island for the music festival." Triton looked at the dark shape.

Lucy looked puzzled. "Are we going to go out and swim some more?" She pointed at the ceiling where the doors were.

"No, this time everybody is going; so we don't have to swim." Triton looked around the hall.

Then Lucy remembered what she wanted to know. "Does the hall move?" she asked.

"Yes." Triton looked at the dark shape again.

"How does it do that?" Lucy was staring at the shape too.

"I'm afraid I can't explain it to you." Triton stroked his beard. "It's one of the things I haven't studied yet. I only know it does. Maybe I'll be able to find someone who can tell you how it works." He looked around at the other mer-people, but he did not move. "I'll have to wait until later. We are getting ready to go on shore."

16

The mer-people were all swimming in line up toward the doors and onto the roof. Triton got in line with Sabrina, while Lucy followed Thetis. Daniel had gone somewhere else. They all swam out into the warm green water and headed toward the surface. They were moving toward the dark shape.

When Lucy got her head above water, she could see that the shape was an island with palm trees growing on it. It was out in the middle of the empty ocean. There was a stream from it flowing down into the sea. The mer-people were starting to swim up the stream.

Lucy could see that there were other mer-people who did not belong to their hall. They were coming from the other side of the island. Lucy took hold of Thetis's tail. She did not want to get lost in the crowd. They all swam up the stream, which took them into a lake.

The lake was so clear that Lucy could see down to the pink bottom. The water was full of mer-people. And there were other mer-people sitting on the shore under the palm trees. Lucy could not tell how many there were.

The mer-people all seemed to be happy. They kept swimming up to other people, slapping them on the back, and laughing. Everybody was talking. Lucy was careful not to let go of Thetis's tail. She was glad to see Triton and Sabrina swimming toward them. Proteus was with them. This morning he had turned a pale green color.

"Proteus is going to take Lucy to meet King Neptune." Triton was speaking to Thetis. "We'll all follow along."

Proteus rose up on his tail and bowed to Lucy. Then he sank back into the water. He told Lucy to take hold of his tail. She was a little bit scared of Proteus. He was so big, and he looked so old. But Thetis told her it was all right. Thetis took hold of Lucy's tail.

They swam up the lake. And as they passed, people moved aside to let them by. They came to a big palm tree with a pink rock under it that was shaped like a chair. On the rock sat the biggest merman Lucy had ever seen. He must have been even bigger than an elephant. Like Proteus he was pale green in color. And he had a long curly beard that covered him all the way down to his lap.

On either side of him beautiful mermaids were sitting on the rocks. Proteus

said something to one of them. She went and spoke to the huge merman. Then she came back to Proteus.

"Neptune will see you now. Don't be afraid." Proteus swam to a place in front of Neptune and lifted Lucy out of the water. He raised her up and handed her to Neptune. Neptune held her on the palm of his hand and moved her up close to his face. Some of the hair from Neptune's beard got tangled around Lucy. She sneezed and almost fell off Neptune's hand. Lucy was so scared and so worried about falling that all she could see was Neptune's enormous nose. She felt dizzy, as if she were in an elevator.

Neptune smiled at Lucy. She did not like to be so close to his huge teeth. But she tried to smile back. She was hoping he would not eat her.

"I'm glad to meet you, Lucy." Neptune let the hand with Lucy on it move down to his lap. From there Lucy had trouble seeing anything. Neptune's beard was all around her. But she felt a little safer. Only, she could not think of anything to say. She tried smiling some more.

"I have heard how you saved Triton." Neptune's voice sounded like thunder. "It is not often that land people are good to sea people. We will always remember you. And our poets will make songs about you. You will always be welcome at the bottom of the sea." Neptune bowed his head at Lucy.

Lucy said, "Thank you. I'm having a nice visit." Then Neptune lowered Lucy down to where Proteus could reach her. He had to untangle her from his beard before he could hand her back. All the mer-people clapped. And one of the mermaidens came swimming up with a little coral crown. She put the crown on Lucy's head. That made the people clap some more.

Proteus led Lucy and Thetis and Triton and Sabrina to a place by the side of the lake where there was room for them to sit on a rock.

"The music is about to begin. You will be able to hear well from here." Proteus stood up on his tail again and bowed. Then he swam away. Lucy noticed that Daniel was back with them. He sat on the rock beside her.

17

Everyone was quiet. In the water no one was playing any more. Far up the lake, where Neptune was, Lucy could see something moving. Several mermaids were swimming toward her. And as they came, they were singing. It was a lovely song that seemed to be about a silver swan. Lucy could not hear the words very well. But the music made her feel happy inside. As she listened, she sat very still and forgot about Neptune. She looked at the ripples in the water and listened to the music. The mermaids went on singing as they swam down the lake. Their song got fainter and fainter.

Lucy looked back to where Neptune was sitting. More mermaids were starting to swim toward her. It was like a parade. While everyone was looking at the mermaids, Daniel poked Lucy. "Look what I have," he whispered.

Lucy looked around at Daniel. He was holding a little plastic bag of hard candies that looked as big as golf balls. "Where did you get that?" Lucy whispered back.

"It fell out of a ship a while ago. I found it falling through the water." Daniel opened the bag and held it out to Lucy. "Have one."

Lucy took a red candy and held it in her hand. Daniel picked out a green one and licked it. Looking at the candy made Lucy think she was hungry. But just then she heard the new group of mermaids singing. As she listened, she let the hand holding the candy rest in her lap. This time the words of the song were all strange. Perhaps they were in another language. Once again the music gave her a drowsy, happy feeling. As long as the mermaids sang, she forgot everything else.

But then Daniel poked her again. He was running his tongue over his candy and pointing to the red ball in her hand.

Lucy held it up and looked at it. As she held it, her mouth began to water. In her mind she could taste raspberries. Slowly, she began to move the piece of sugar toward her waiting tongue.

Just then Thetis touched her shoulder. "Watch out, Lucy," she said. "Don't forget. If you eat anything while you are here you may have to stay."

The color of raspberries began to creep over Lucy's face. Her fingers went limp. She stopped breathing and let the candy wobble down the rock into the water.

"It would be lovely if you would stay with us." Thetis slipped her arm around

Lucy. "But you ought to stay of your own free will. Daniel was wicked to trick you."

Lucy peeked at Daniel. He was staring up the lake as if he had not heard a word.

Triton came wiggling over to Lucy and Thetis. He said nothing about the candy. "It's almost time for Lucy to go home. Neptune has promised to send her by air."

Lucy looked at Neptune where he sat on his pink chair stroking his beard. Though he was too far away for her to be sure, he seemed to be smiling. She looked all around, but there was no airplane to be seen. In a tiny voice, she asked, "Won't I ever see you again?"

"Do you really want to see us again?" Triton looked so pleased that Lucy began to feel better. As she smiled a little, Triton turned to Thetis. "You haven't seen Lucy's green lake. Maybe we could plan a visit. What do you say?"

Thetis did not say anything.

"Maybe month after next. What do you think?" He waited for Thetis to answer.

Thetis sat for a while and stared at her tail. Then she said, "I can't decide right now."

"All right." Triton patted Lucy's shoulder. "We'll try to come if we can."

"How will I know you're there?" Lucy looked from Triton to Thetis.

"Come to the lake month after next on the day before the full moon and sing us a song. But don't sing if there is anybody else around." He pointed his finger at her. "If we are there we will swim to your rock. Maybe Sabrina will come too." Triton stroked Sabrina's hand. For the first time Sabrina smiled at Lucy.

"When is the day before the full moon?" Lucy wrinkled up her forehead.

"Watch the moon every night. You'll soon know. Start tonight. Where you live there'll be a full moon again. The moon will be a little smaller tomorrow. Before long you'll be an old hand." Triton looked up at a small cloud.

"May I bring Nancy when I come?" Lucy looked at Triton.

"Who is Nancy?" Triton frowned a little.

"She's my friend." Lucy said. "You would like her. We do everything together."

"Well, all right," said Triton. "Any friend of yours is a friend of ours. But promise you won't tell any grown-ups." Triton looked her in the eye when he said, "Promise."

Lucy's face began to grow pink again. But she sat up straight and said, "I promise."

Just then a dark cloud passed in front of the sun. Triton and Thetis looked at the cloud. "We have to leave now."

Thetis kissed Lucy good-bye and slipped into the water.

Triton took her hand. "Don't be scared, Lucy. We have to let you go home by yourself. But you will be safe. Neptune is your friend." Triton squeezed her hand and followed Thetis.

Sabrina was already in the lake where all the other mer-people were waving

good-bye. Sabrina waved too, but Daniel was not there.

Lucy sat alone watching the sky grow darker and darker. The mer-people had dived under the water. And there was no one left except Neptune, sitting high on his chair, looking at Lucy. His cheeks were puffed out as if he were blowing.

Before long the sky was so dark that Lucy could not see. In the blackness she could hear the wind howling, but she did not feel any wind. "Don't be scared," Triton had said. Lucy tried not to be afraid.

18

The wind was so loud it made Lucy dizzy. All she could hear was the roaring noise. Again she had the funny feeling of going up and up in an elevator.

The howling went on and on. Lucy thought it would never stop. But little by little it began to fade away. Slowly the blackness turned to grayness. Dim shapes formed that looked like trees. And a soft breeze moved her hair. Then she heard a new sound, the sound of a bell. It was going, "Bing-bong, bing-bong, bing-bong, bing-bong." After that a clock began to strike. "One, two, three, four, five." It must be the campus clock striking five o'clock.

All of a sudden Lucy could see again. She was still sitting on a rock, but now it was a cold, gray rock. Around the lake in front of her the trees were no longer palm trees. And in the water she saw her old friends, the water bugs dancing as always.

Lucy looked down where her tail had been and saw only her blue jeans and her white sneakers. She was sitting on her favorite rock beside the green lake. A few drops of rain began to wet her face. She put up a hand to feel her hair and brushed something off the top of her head. A bit of pink coral fell into her lap. It was almost a perfect circle and might have been a little crown — just big enough for a doll. Lucy slipped it into her pocket.

In spite of the raindrops, Lucy did not move. She kept sitting there looking at the trees and the water, feeling strange. Finally, the cold made her get up. She picked up the empty can that she had used for slugs and started along the path toward home.

As she walked through the woods, she kept looking down at her legs. How good to have legs again. She wiggled her toes and lifted her knee.

Everything went on looking queer, as if she were in a different country. When she came to where people were walking, the people looked strange. But nobody paid any attention to her. All the way home she felt as if she were walking in a dream. The cars on the road looked funny. The road up to her house looked funny. She kept seeing things she had never noticed before.

As she climbed the hill, she looked up at the sky. It was too soon yet for the moon. She would go to bed early and watch from her bedroom window as the full moon came over the trees.

The kitchen had the warm smell of

baked beans. Her mother was setting the table the same as usual. "Oh, here you are, Lucy," she said. "I'm glad you got home before the storm."

Lucy looked out of the window. But the sky was clear. In the distance there was only one small cloud melting away.

Her mother looked where Lucy was looking. "It seems to be clearing up. I thought a terrible storm was coming. There was an awful wind. And everything went black. Didn't you see it?"

Lucy did not answer. She felt the lump in her pocket where the little piece of coral was.

Her mother went on talking. "Wash your hands. I want you to finish this job for me." As she talked, she began to tear up lettuce. "While you were out, Nancy phoned. They're back from their trip. You won't have to mope around by yourself any more."

Lucy was only half listening. She turned on the kitchen tap and stared at the little cloud. Then she looked at the silver water running over her hands. Where does this water come from, she wondered?

The Forsaken Merman

Come, dear children, let us away;
  Down and away below!
Now my brothers call from the bay;
Now the great winds shoreward blow;
Now the salt tides seaward flow;
Now the wild white horses play,
Champ and chafe and toss in the spray.
Children dear, let us away!
This way, this way!

Call her once before you go —
Call once yet!
In a voice that she will know:
'Margaret! Margaret!'
Children's voices should be dear
(Call once more) to a mother's ear;
Children's voices, wild with pain —
Surely she will come again!
Call her once and come away;
This way, this way!
'Mother dear, we cannot stay!'
The wild white horses foam and fret.
Margaret! Margaret!

Come, dear children, come away down!
Call no more!
One last look at the white-wall'd town,
And the little grey church on the windy shore;
Then come down.
She will not come though you call all day.
Come away, come away!

Children dear, was it yesterday
We heard the sweet bells over the bay?
In the caverns where we lay,
Through the surf and through the swell,
The far-off sound of a silver bell?
Sand-strewn caverns, cool and deep,
Where the winds are all asleep;
Where the spent lights quiver and gleam;
Where the salt weed sways in the stream;
Where the sea-beasts ranged all round
Feed in the ooze of their pasture-ground;
Where the sea-snakes coil and twine,
Dry their mail and bask in the brine;
Where great whales come sailing by,
Sail and sail, with unshut eye,
Round the world for ever and aye?
When did music come this way?
Children dear, was it yesterday?

Children dear, was it yesterday
(Call yet once) that she went away?
Once she sate with you and me,
On a red gold throne in the heart of the sea,
And the youngest sate on her knee.
She comb'd its bright hair, and she tended it well,
When down swung the sound of the far-off bell.
She sigh'd, she look'd up through the clear green sea;
She said: 'I must go, for my kinsfolk pray
In the little grey church on the shore to-day.
'Twill be Easter-time in the world — ah me!
And I lose my poor soul, Merman! here with thee.'
I said: 'Go up, dear heart, through the waves!
Say thy prayer, and come back to the kind sea-caves!'
She smiled, she went up through the surf in the bay.
Children dear, was it yesterday?

Children dear, were we long alone?
'The sea grows stormy, the little ones moan.
Long prayers,' I said, 'in the world they say.

Come!' I said; and we rose through the surf in the bay.
We went up the beach, by the sandy down
Where the sea-stocks bloom, to the white-wall'd town;
Through the narrow paved streets, where all was still,
To the little grey church on the windy hill.
From the church came a murmur of folk at their
prayers,
But we stood without in the cold blowing airs.
We climb'd on the graves, on the stones, worn with
rains,
And we gazed up the aisle through the small-leaded
panes.
She sate by the pillar; we saw her clear;
'Margaret, hist! come quick, we are here.
Dear heart,' I said, 'we are long alone;
The sea grows stormy, the little ones moan.'
But, ah, she gave me never a look,
For her eyes were seal'd to the holy book!
Loud prays the priest; shut stands the door.
Come away, children, call no more!
Come away, come down, call no more!

Down, down, down!
Down to the depths of the sea!
She sits at her wheel in the humming town,
Singing most joyfully.
Hark what she sings: 'O joy, O joy,
For the humming street, and the child with its toy!
For the priest, and the bell, and the holy well —
For the wheel where I spun,
And the blessed light of the sun!'
And so she sings her fill,
Singing most joyfully,
Till the shuttle falls from her hand,
And the whizzing wheel stands still.
She steals to the window, and looks at the sand,
And over the sand at the sea;
And her eyes are set in a stare;
And anon there breaks a sigh,
And anon there drops a tear,
From a sorrow-clouded eye,
And a heart sorrow-laden,
A long, long sigh;
For the cold strange eyes of a little Mermaiden,
And the gleam of her golden hair.

Come away, away children
Come children, come down!
The hoarse wind blows colder;
Lights shine in the town.
She will start from her slumber
When gusts shake the door;
She will hear the winds howling,
Will hear the waves roar.
We shall see, while above us
The waves roar and whirl,
A ceiling of amber,
A pavement of pearl.
Singing: 'Here came a mortal,
But faithless was she!
And alone dwell for ever
The kings of the sea.'

But, children, at midnight,
When soft the winds blow,
When clear falls the moonlight,
When spring-tides are low;

When sweet airs come seaward
From heaths starr'd with broom.
And high rocks throw mildly
On the blanch'd sands a gloom;
Up the still, glistening beaches,
Up the creeks we will hie,
Over banks of bright seaweed
The ebb-tide leaves dry.
We will gaze, from the sand-hills,
At the white, sleeping town;
At the church on the hill-side —
And then come back down.
Singing: 'There dwells a loved one,
But cruel is she!
She left lonely for ever
The kings of the sea.'

— MATTHEW ARNOLD